FISH (

...ng Book
by Carole Markin

Fish Out of Water is a collection of fish and sea life images inspired by the drawings Carole created for a series of whimsical and fanciful 3-D aquariums. This led to an 8 foot backlit piece called "Fish Out of Water," installed in the lobby of the Orthopedic Hospital for Children in Los Angeles. The piece was funded by a grant from the Cultural Affairs Department of the City of Los Angeles for public art works.

These underwater creatures have personality - such as distinctive eyes and sly smiles - and are spirited, whimsical, inviting, free and fun. Be imaginative when you fill in the fish, seaweed and backgrounds. You don't need to stay within the lines. Have fun! You are swimming in an undersea, dream world.

ISBN: 978-0-578-56082-3

Cover Image and Design: Carole Markin

www.fishoutofwatercoloringbook.com

Printed in the United States of America

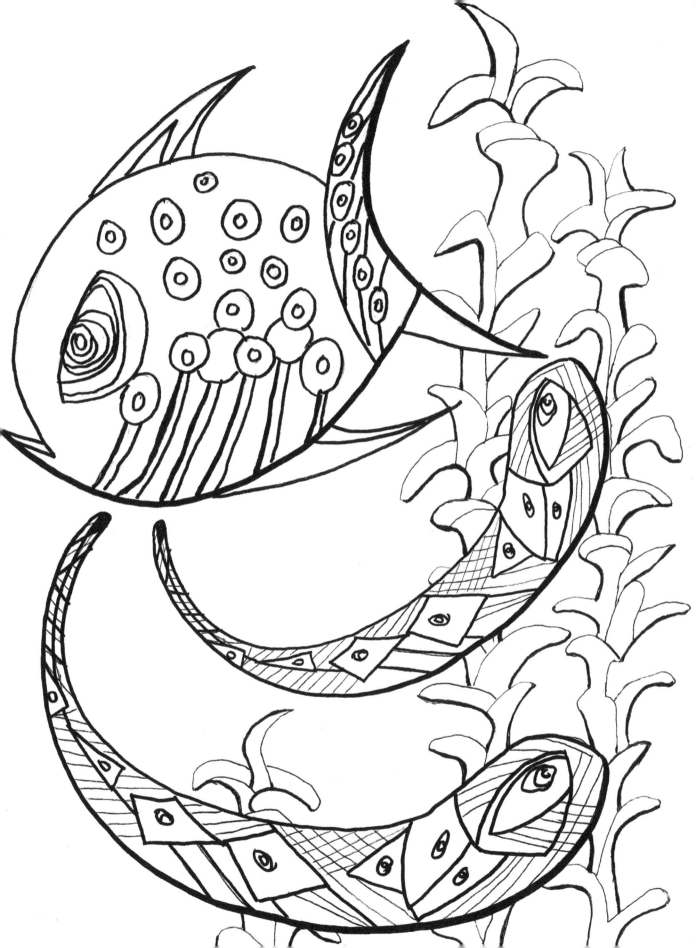

CPSIA information can be obtained
at www.ICGtesting.com
Printed in the USA
LVHW021156210520
656047LV00007B/48